S0-AVJ-186

100 PARADES

MOLLY FISK
Editor

To Bachan and Papa
Love Hana
My poem is on page 37!

2000
California Poets in the Schools
Statewide Anthology

© 2000 California Poets in the Schools
All Rights Reserved/Printed in California

CALIFORNIA
POETS IN THE
SCHOOLS

Cover collage by Christine Irving

Cover design by Susanna Wilson, Grass Valley, CA

Book design by Wordsworth, San Geronimo, CA

Printing by KNI, Anaheim, CA

ISBN # 0-939927-17-9

This anthology is dedicated with love and thanks to
Susan Sibbet and Gina Mackintosh

Directors on the board of California Poets in the Schools have contributed cash, expertise, and community connections to help the program grow and improve over the past 36 years. Two people's dedication stands out in this distinguished crowd. Gina Mackintosh and Susan Sibbet, who have consistently given their time, care, and resources to help the organization in a time of transition. Over the past four years, they have met every month and worked every week to keep the organization vital and growing. For this we offer congratulations and thanks and we invite them to be the Grand Marshals of this year's poetry parades.

California Poets in the Schools is grateful to the hundreds of individuals, foundations, and agencies who graciously offer their support:

ANGEL:
Anonymous
Theodore Seton

BENEFACTORS:
Lee Doan
Miss Barbara Ann Frank
Susan Kline
Allan Lasher
Stephanie Mendel
Constance Miller
John Morton & Laura Donnelley-
 Morton
Susan & David Sibbet
Louise Wendell, Sr.

PATRONS:
Daryl & Phyllis Chinn
Alison Geballe
Dave & Amy Nelson
Jean Schulz
Ruth & Dunham Sherer
Lilla & Andrew Weinberger
Christine Wendel & Judith Bailie
Jim & Elaine Wolf

LEADERS:
John & Paula Gambs
Natalie & Irvin Gendler
Jane Kaplan
Gina Mackintosh
Nion & Ira McEvoy
M. L. Harrison Mackie
Charles & Nancy McLaughlin
Brenda Pentland
Susan Sterling
Judith Stronach
Judith Taylor
Thomas & Janet Van Dyck
Amy Wendel

SPONSORS:
Arnold Aaron
Michael Adler
Stephen C. Bieneman
Wendy Breuer
Daniel Brockman
Patricia Brown
John Carol
Elizabeth & Park Chamberlain
Jeffrey & Elena Clark

Carla Cogan
David Conston, M.D.
Stanley Conston
Robert Cox
Paul & Joanne Cummings
Dwight & Jean Davis
Betty Denton
Basil DePinto
Albert F. DeSilver
Harrison DeSilver
Sandra Dijkstra
Dr. Ramona Doyle
"Uncle" Don Fanning & Carol Kent
 Ireland
Henry & Priscilla Fiola
Sidney Frank
J. Ruth Gendler
Elizabeth Kelley Gillogly
Judith Ghidinelli & Sharon Page
 Ritchie
Enid & Martin Gleich
Paula Gocker
Dale & Phillip Going
Ronda Gomez-Quinones
Janet Grande
Surlene Grant
Jonathan Halperin & Felicia Wong
Arthur & Betty Hausman
Rachel Higgins
Maria & Warren Higgins
Kenneth Hill
Mary Gary Harrison
Alison Hyder
Leroy Hunt
George & Sylvia Johnson
Peder & Nancy Jones
Lynne Kaufman
Bruce W. Leppla
Karen Lewis
Raymond Lifchez
Jennifer Lloyd
Fred Lonsdale
Lynn & David Loux
Ann & Karl Ludwig
Diane Lutovich
Dorothy Lykes
K. A. McCord
Greg & Kathy Moe and Jon Watson
Karin Moe
Delia Moon
Jackie Mundell

Carmel S. D. Naraval
Patricia Nichols
Chris Olander
Felicia Oldfather
Reathe Joy Oliver
Mary Pallares
Allon Rafael
Stephen Rentmeesters
Mr. & Mrs. Royal Robbins
Ivy & Leigh Robinson
Mary Lou Robinson
Jill & Paul Robinson
Elizabeth Rosenberg
Faye Rosenzweig
Leo & Deborah Ruth
Laurel Nicholes Sargent
Pamela & Harold Schneider
Don Shanley
Stella Shao
Brian Smith & Alison McLean
Kathleen Soto
David Spina
Lani Steele
Sol Stern
Gretchen Stone
Jean Sward
Roselyn Swig
Edith & Robert Tannenbaum
Natasha & Greg Terk
David & Susan Terris
Celeste Teters
Jean-Louise Thacher
Beth Thomasy & Dan Shvodian
Quincy Troupe
Karen Wendel

Special thanks to the foundations who make this anthology possible:
Manuel and Rhoda Mayerson
    Foundation
Zellerbach Family Fund

We wish to acknowledge the support of the following Government, Corporate and Foundation supporters who have made our poetry residencies, anthologies, and conferences possible:
California Arts Council
California Casualty Group
Chase Manhattan Foundation
City Arts and Lectures
Community Foundation of Santa
    Barbara
Cooper, White and Cooper LLP
Dean Witter Foundation
Golden Dragon Printing
Good Works Foundation
Grove Consultants International
Insurance Industry Charitable Fund
Lannan Foundation
Marin Community Foundation
Miranda Lux Foundation
National Endowment for the Arts
Orrick, Herrington and Sutcliffe LLP
Potrero Nuevo Fund
San Francisco Arts Commission
San Francisco Department of
    Children, Youth and their Families
Silver Giving Foundation
Stern Memorial Trust
St. Paul Companies, Inc.
The ArtCouncil, Inc.
Valley Foundation
Walter and Elise Haas Fund
William and Flora Hewlett
    Foundation

AND:
100's of Poet-Teachers
100's of Contributors
1000's of California Schools,
    Teachers, and Parents
1000's of K-12 students throughout
    California

TABLE OF CONTENTS

INTRODUCTION:
A PARADE OF OUR OWN

by Gary Soto

When we think of parades we think of floats, marching bands, prancing horses, fluttering flags, girl scouts and boy scouts, a military drill team, and girls twirling batons pitched repeatedly into the air. We think of polished fire engines and vintage cars in which sit the mayor and the mayor's wife or husband, the equivalent of a king and queen. We may also think of the beauty queen waving her hand back and forth, back and forth. Boy, she must be tired!

But what about marching poems? Is it possible for poems to put on legs and march in their own parade? If you're a poet, yes, it is possible. You can assemble such a parade. The spectacle, of course, is something of the mind, or the imagination, but it is just as believable as the real thing. After all, when we close our eyes, don't we see pictures behind our eyelids? Aren't these the same as the real world?

So we have our own parade in this very busy, very loud, very handsome anthology. The poems come from San Francisco and Los Angeles, and from places in between. Some of the poems are about birds, the Pacific Ocean, stones, snow, trees — the tangible world. Other poems are about secrets, romance, forgiveness, sadness, prayers — the not so tangible. Some of the poems are about the everyday — cars, Valentine's Day, and regular ole moms and dads. There is sadness in some of the poems, and happiness in others. There is, in short, a balance of living in which a barometer of emotions go from hot to cold. There are poems which stop us to reflect. I'm thinking of "Mom is like a barracuda," by Alex Martin, and the part that has nothing to do with mom. No, I'm thinking of the end of the poem when Alex describes himself as "a city with no echo." My hair lifted when I read that line. I understood that at that moment in which he was composing the poem, Alex was bodily a city and no heart was pounding within him. No, the heart had stopped. I hope, of course, that it started again.

And how curious for me to discover a poem by a friend — Lani Goto, a high school student I once knew as a baby. I remember reading her some stories of mine thirteen years ago, and now Lani, a young lady, is writing poetry? I knew that she drew (I have a drawing of hers executed when she was six years old), and played piano and Celtic harp. But poetry, too? Wow! She was such a little girl when I met her and now she's arranging words on the page? I single Lani out because I know her. And I have gotten to know the other writers — Juliana, Marta, Josh, Ashley, Katrina, Bowman, and others, among others — via their poetry. It's as if I had met them and, in fact, I am their confidant, a friend so to speak. They have told me so much about themselves and are not in the least embarrassed by what they have to share.

What we have here is a wonderful collection of verse done by young people. They serve as example for adults what it means to be creative. Under rain or no rain I hope you enjoy this parade.

EDITOR'S NOTE:
THE SPICE OF LIFE

In my small town on the Fourth of July, there is a parade. It's the usual American affair: decorated floats with Girl Scouts, a politician or two, the fire department, horse-drawn carriages, vintage cars. The Rotary, Soroptimist, and Elks clubs get into the act, and both high school marching bands. There are many awkward stops and starts as an act outpaces the one in front and has to march in place for a while. Horses choose to lift their tails at awkward moments, and the packed streets reverberate with talk and laughter and enthusiastic, if intermittent, applause.

Nowadays, we also have some modern entries: the local gymnastics teachers put parallel bars on a float and their students do amazing flips and turns while the entire contraption drives slowly down Broad Street. There is a Jazzercise class whose leotard-clad members (mostly middle-aged women of amazingly varied shapes and sizes) shimmy and shake in formation down the road. There's a belly-dancing contingent. One year a rock and roll band played on a platform borne by a huge fork-lift, the gears grinding in tune to the music, the whole shebang lifted and lowered about twenty feet in the air in time to the beat of the drums. It was a terrifying sight.

But this madness doesn't just happen on the Fourth of July. There's also a parade in early September celebrating the California state constitution's anniversary. Veterans of World War II, Korea, Viet Nam, and the Gulf march on Memorial Day. We celebrate Mardi Gras in February with the Joe Cain Day parade (no, I don't know who he was either). And during our annual literary festival, a long line of letters of the alphabet carried by school children prances down the street to celebrate the written word.

I go to every single parade, I can't help it. Whether earnest or tongue-in-cheek, corny or tear-inducing, each one verges on a kind of beauty. The variety of people, floats, zany costumes, attitudes — the air of celebration or solemn honor — makes my heart sing. There is something quintessential to our culture about taking all this individuality and making of it a shared, communal event.

And that (to make this long story a little shorter) is also why I love this year's anthology of poems from California students and their teachers, *100 Parades*. The strength of each individual voice — on such a wide range of subjects and with so many variations in style — is brought together into one chorus celebrating our world. There's something gripping to me about the idea of all those different teachers, carrying only their love for poems and the lesson plans they've invented (oh yeah, and lots of support from the main office and our generous donors), striding into grade schools and middle schools and high schools all over California, into alternative schools and after-school programs and juvenile halls, all bearing the radical idea that poetry is useful, that language was meant to be played with and shared, that everyone has something to say, and that every individual voice, raised high, is valuable. If this isn't patriotism, what is?

Sometimes, at the end of our Fourth of July parade, the folksinger and labor historian U. Utah Phillips will grab the microphone and ask everyone to sing "The People's National Anthem." This isn't *America*, or *The Star Spangled Banner*, or any of the songs you remember singing in school or at ballgames. This is something I think he made up, and I'm going to tell you all how to do it right now:

OK, everyone stand up and place your right hand over your heart. Now, on the count of three, begin to sing, as loud as you can, your own favorite song. Ready? One, two, *three*!!

— *Molly Fisk, Editor*

STUDENT POEMS

UNTITLED

Watch how an apple rots
It looks more and more like the moon.

Josh Tshihamba, First Grade
MacGregor Primary, Albany
Judith Tannenbaum, Poet-Teacher

ON THE TITANIC

The screams were loud as a hundred parades.
The water was like scorpions whipping your skin.
All those people died.
They didn't even try to breathe.
Their eyes were lit with tears.
You could hear their tears banging on the floor
even from a mile away.
Bang, bang, their tears went
as their hearts plunged into the sea.
All of their last words were the same:
"I'll love my family forever and ever."

Bowman McNear, Second Grade
Wade Thomas Elementary, San Anselmo
Robin Jacobson, Poet-Teacher

ANG PAGGAWWA NG BAHAY NG ESTRELLANG KUMIKINANG

Una'y hahanap ng bulcan
Punuin ng ssahig na apoy
Lagyuan dingding na pulang rosas
Kausapin ang buwang lagyuan ng atip
Ang ulap ay chimneya
Kulog at kidlat angtubig
Ang araw ay ang electrika.
Anghangi ay mga bintana at pintuan
Dragon, anghel, mgga tao, ibon, Pañginoon, ang mga kaibigan
Lahat ay inaanyayahan sa Bahay ng Estrellang Kumikinang.

[Translated into Tagalog]

HOW TO BUILD A HOUSE FOR SHOOTING STARS

First you find a volcano
Put in a foundation of fresh water
Pour in a floor of fire
Raise walls of red roses
Ask the moon to provide the roof.
A cloud is the chimney, thunder and lightning for water pipes.
The sun gives the electrical wiring
The wind is our windows and our doors
Dragons, Angels, People, Birds, God, Our Best Friends
All are welcome in the House of Shooting Stars.

Voices of the First and Second Grades, Phillipine bilingual class
Longfellow Elementary, San Francisco
JoNelle Toriseva, Poet-Teacher

THE BIRD POEM

Robin, why are you so red?
When I was a baby
my feathers were inside me
and blood got on them.
Then, they grew out to be as red as lava
the mud from the cow got on my back
        and made it brown.

Now I fly to the South
to find food in the wintertime.

Eagle, how do you hunt so well?
Because I fly so fast
that sometimes I even don't know
where I'm going
but when I see a rat in the field
I swoop down and trap it
with my claws like a bear.

Bluejay, bluejay, why are you so blue?
I drank too much water
and it made me feel sad.
My Mom got mad
and I started to cry.
Then I went to sleep
and I dreamed I was all blue.
        And I am.

Voices of the First and Second Grades
Manchester Elementary, Manchester
Scott Meltsner, Poet-Teacher

UNTITLED

A screw looks
like
a ballerina
twirling
through a glass
stage.
It looks
like a pencil
dying to
write.
Or a
flashlight
waiting to shine.

Roxie Perkins, Second Grade
Marin School, Albany
Judith Tannenbaum, Poet-Teacher

UNTITLED

Ocean quiet but loud
Whale leaping to the heavens from
the depths of the sea, still whistling
The sea as quiet as a pond in fall
          a path of bubbles repeating itself
forever and ever the whale blowing
          blowing and like paintings of
the angels

Kendall Owings, Second Grade
Lakeshore Elementary, San Francisco
Grace Grafton, Poet-Teacher

PRAYER FOR THE GREAT FAMILY

Gratitude to the great sun that gives light,
Gratitude to the air we breathe,
Gratitude to water for salmon to swim in and for drinking,
Gratitude to maidenhair fern swaying on the golden streets,
Gratitude to earthworms digging tunnels, making soil,
Gratitude to the oak tree giving acorns to the squirrels,
Gratitude to bats eating apples, planting trees,
Gratitude to colorful wildflowers attracting butterflies,
Gratitude to the lizard basking in the sun,
Gratitude to cock robin who sings like an orchestra in the
    window,
Gratitude to the willow tree underneath the moonlight,
Gratitude to salmon jumping over the dam like birds,
Gratitude to the red tailed hawk swirling through green clouds,
Gratitude to deer whose spots are balls of snow that sometimes
    fall in winter,
Gratitude to cute otter who cracks open shells with rocks,
Gratitude to bluetail fox leaping through the bushes,
Gratitude to bunny that marches through the snow,
Gratitude to deer that glitters in the moonlight,
Gratitude to trout whose wisdom is superior,
Gratitude to frogs and newts for forgiving us.

**Alex, Brittney, Derek, Dylan, Emilie, Gabriella, Johany,
Justin, Kane, Karen, Kim, Kieran, Michelle, Nitsa,
Rachel, Sarah, Tanner, Taylor & Will, Third Grade**
Manor School, Fairfax
Albert DeSilver, Poet-Teacher

The end (of poetry)

The end is like a song that once went
a million miles that stopped with
the sun saying no, to go inside a person
and see another person and going inside
him or her seeing another and another
and another then to stop — it's empty
and there is nothing else to say yes, like
a candle burning out by the touch
of god, like a bird's wing dying
out of power, going out of the bird,
out of the candle out of god
out of saying yes going out of empty
out of that person and that person
out of the sun saying no
out of a million miles out of a song
that was never put to sleep.

Alyssa Young, Third Grade
Laguna Blanca School, Santa Barbara
Perie Longo, Poet-Teacher

UNTITLED

Trees as big as the sky.
Sophia to my right. Kristen to my left.
The clouds are trying to make me think by
making shapes. Chips of wood. Getting kicked around.
I see trash around the road. Nature by itself.
Shadows on the ground. Trees holding hands.
Sophia writing on paper. Kristen looking around.
Clouds helping the rainbow stand up. Molly
rainbow. The rainbow reflects off Molly's glasses.
The wood sits on the world. Trash everywhere.
Nature looking at me. Shadows disappear. Tree
standing still. Sophia. Her long blond hair. Kristen.
Thinking what to write. Clouds. Puffy as can be.
Wood. Likes to jump. Trash. I hope it goes away.
Nature is all around. Shadows. Are gone.

Molly Abram, Third Grade
Lakeshore Elementary, San Francisco
Grace Grafton, Poet-Teacher

FIXING THE CAR

My father's hands
are greasy and oily
from working on his car
in the garage.
He is using a ratchet
and he asks me
to hand him a tool.
I get it and he says,
"Thank you."
His hands are like
black clouds on a rainy day.
I ask, "Dad, what are you
fixing under the car?"
"It's not too far," he answers.

Alan Wells, Third Grade
Lincoln Acres Elementary, National City
Glory Foster, Poet-Teacher

UNTITLED

I come from the lake
I am the salmon that wakes up
before sunlight

My name is Licica
I am like the sky blue
and the dark black beetle that
crawls along the wall of the lake

My friends are the butterfly
that flies above the water each morning
And the blue bird that sings
on the long branch

My mom is the apple tree
that grows near the house.
My dad is the big tree
as tall as the sky.

My sister is the sky
that flies with the bird.
My brother is the ocean
that swims with the dolphins
and talks to the whales.

Licica Cervantes, Third Grade
Point Arena Elementary, Point Arena
Karen Lewis, Poet-Teacher

STONE

I would like to go into a stone.
Not to be taken, but to rest.
My smooth sides make friends with others.
No matter where I go, time flies
by and by and away.
Things rub side to side
but I don't mind.
My colors are from the outside.
Things come and go
but I stay right here.
My beautiful sound goes with
the flow of the afternoon river.
I travel the world by hand.
And the world is my great home.

Cody Cunnington, Third Grade
Wade Thomas School, San Anselmo
Karen Benke, Poet-Teacher

SECRETS

Turquoise laughter
An eagle in the sky
A butterfly whispering in
A dragonfly's ear
The angels peering in
The corner window
Just like a poet weaving
Her story
On a loom of sawdust.

Caroline Calhoun, Fourth Grade
Neil Cummins School, Corte Madera
Karen Benke, Poet-Teacher

ODE TO LIFE

Ode to life,
A precious wonder,
A miracle that comes true,
Something that every human, animal, every living creature
goes through.

Hold life together with two of your fingers.
Examine it closely. What do you see? ...
A girl feeling happiness,
A boy with a fear,
A kind young woman with love in her heart,
A poet writing a poem about all these things.

Put life up to your ear. What do you hear?
Laughing, crying,
Screaming,
Everything there is to hear.

Look through your eyes and see life
With all the colors of the rainbow.
Hear life with all the sounds there are to hear.
Feel life with every emotion.

Marta Yushprakh, Fourth/Fifth Grade
Stanton Elementary, Castro Valley
Janice De Ruiter, Poet-Teacher

Soft Gold

Rainy days
flow with memories
such magical castles
waiting for life.

Rain going down softly
can't let me go.
My heart is happy
like a mountain joy.

Rainy days are a beautiful sight
full of wonders,
rainbows on the side,
shapes full of colors.

Be free like the wind
through the air,
like spikes through a horn.
A tunnel goes with the wind
such mysterious songs,
tradition, tunnels tickling along
like golden canes
jumping with laughter.

A heart full of wonders
sometimes a place
where I am.

Rainy days are the best.
I wish I was alone.
The rainy memories flying along,
swallow me, romantic days.
Hearts full of joy and love,
two sisters staying together
like two faces that can't stand alone.

Victoria Kim, Fourth/Fifth Grade
Stanton Elementary, Castro Valley
Janice De Ruiter, Poet-Teacher

MY SPIRIT IS A DEAD INDIAN WOMAN

who worked in the desert plains
      cooked the corn
            and sewed her children's clothes

            In the early mornings
      her husband
            climbed on his graceful horse
      to check the fields
            coming back at the stroke of dusk . . .
if there were such things.
            Down he sits for supper (or dinner)
next to his children, if I am correct
six children.
            Three little boys next to the father
and three little girls with skyblue ribbons
in their hair,
sitting next to the mother . . .
who I often talk to
            through a rock that my father
made float
                  while a blue woman stood
      on the rock with hair like a
      flowing river and fish
      running through it.
            This woman was my great
grandmother.
            You could say I am
the great granddaughter of the water woman.

Luna Argueta, Fourth Grade
Lakeshore Elementary, San Francisco
Grace Grafton, Poet-Teacher

Born in Music

I was born in music
I was born in a 15 story
trumpet
I been woke
by a bass.
I am a kid that
runs through a harmonica.
I am a wild animal
that plays a guitar.
I am a little baby
that is crying
in the cello.
I am an adult that
is yelling at the kids
in the bongos.

William A. Vail, Fourth Grade
Longfellow Elementary, San Francisco
Julie Gamberg, Poet-Teacher

Poetry is Black and White

I was blind
because I couldn't see
black and white.
I crashed into a wall of words
and they fell off the white paper
into a black pile.
Poetry is the way
I put the words
back in order.

Christian Rodarte, Fourth Grade
Lincoln Acres Elementary, San Diego
Celia Sigmon, Poet-Teacher

Point Reyes: A Secret Beach

A
countless
applause,
the silent
playing of the
sun, the moans
of a heron, sandpipers
scurrying like rolling
rocks, an abalone shell
glittering like jewels,
rough, dry sponges
clinging to boulders,
lacy kelp, and the
silent walking
of the clams.
The seasons
change.
It's
s
p
r
i
n
g
n
o
w
Eggs hatching like popping popcorn.
The secret of wildlife shall be
unexplainable forever.

Jonathan Qvistgaard, Fourth Grade
McNear Elementary, Petaluma
Terri Ehret, Poet-Teacher

EARTH'S SECRETS

is there a tiger
hiding its treasures
of gold and emeralds?
is the sun
as greedy as the tiger,
or is it just a duke of space?

is the earth committing suicide
or do its secrets contain things
it cannot control?
is the king's gravity
stronger than the planets?

does the earth dream
of dying spirits?
are the earth's humans rebelling
for losing control of nature?
is Darkness causing heat;
Darkness resembling humans
in the dreams
of earth's suffering soul?

Ryan Hand, Fourth Grade
Prestwood Elementary, Sonoma
Arthur Dawson, Poet-Teacher

SADNESS

In the darkness
a white coat
moving in the
closet. Someone was
there, I don't
know who, but the
sadness was in my
heart.

Maria Cervantes, Fourth Grade
Sunkist Elementary, Port Hueneme
Shelley Savren, Poet-Teacher

WHAT IF IT NEVER HAPPENED

I sat on a tall oak in the sunshine
a clap of lightning no a branch
breaking the top branch my life
falling with me so I lifted my life
to wishes and turned into a flowing
autumn leaf gold and then tips
of my outstretched veins turned silver
and white falling to a snowflake
like an angel in winter the feathers
grow I am a gold eagle in spring
shining in the morning sun
what if it never happened

Julianna Driskel, Fourth Grade
Mountain View School, Santa Barbara
Perie Longo, Poet-Teacher

MOTHER, MY MOTHER

Scarlett, my mother
as fragile as a butterfly's wing
yet as strong as a winter storm.

Whose hair is the black
threads of night. Who turns
my angry storm clouds into
happy sunshine.

Scarlett, my mother,
mother of mountains and mares.

My mother, who runs like
the winds through lavender fields.

My mother, the whisper of rain.
A great red rose of love
in a great grey desert
of loneliness.

My mother, the silk of China,
the voice of freedom,
the lily of the valley, and
the wings of love.

Mother, my mother,
silver of the moon, red of the sunset,
beauty of a rainbow,
waves of the ocean.

Mother, my mother,
my eyes, my voice, my freedom,
my love.

Andrea Matthews, Grade Four
Monte Vista School, Santa Barbara
Perie Longo, Poet-Teacher

A Man Called the Hermit

Light was thrown through my window,
but I splashed my arms around my curtains
and destroyed the beam from heaven.

Love came to my door and knocked,
but I scolded it, slapped it
and slammed the door in its face.

Hope wanted to help when it came through
my chimney,
but I fell into its trap when it crawled inside me,
made me hollow, decided to stay there,
then made me sad.
I got rid of it; it made me want praise
and affection.

Praise and affection came along too
with a life. I turned them down
and now I'm here inside my house
with no doors nor windows
to the freedom of the outside.

Bianca Licata, Fifth Grade
Neil Cummins School, Corte Madera
Prartho Sereno, Poet-Teacher

THE MAIDEN

I see now.
The moon touches her like magic
Beads of silver and beauty.
I am here in the heart of the ocean.
Immortality,
Fire,
Magic,
Love,
This is what she is made of.
This is what she has
A door
of time!
I must reach it.
I must get through.
I haven't much time left,
She approaches
The images behind
casting a spell as if by the gods.
The night is great.
She speaks,
"The unconscious mind," she says.
She holds out a pearl as if made from crystal
Blue and bright and beautiful.
"Yours," she says.
I don't understand.
I hear one word.
"Go," I hear her say.
I fade.

Michelle Michelbook, Fifth Grade
Vannoy Elementary, Castro Valley
Janice De Ruiter, Poet-Teacher

FIVE WOMEN

Two are talking
      orange
      yellow
      attract
the workers.
      pause
      they
      talk of
      the workers
As they talk of them
      yellow
      draws back
      "No"
      she says
      orange
silently asks
      for
      forgiveness.
      Their mother
glances over
      to
      them
      And remembers
      being
      a child.

One is silent
      grey
      sad
      ugly
no one likes me
      she thinks
      as she draws
          her hand
      to her heart

thinking, remembering
        what had happened
        to change her life
        Her mother
        glances over
                to
        her
        And remembers
        even better.

Two are talking
        blue
        green
        argue
        over nothing
        sisters
            they are
        green
            smells
            the incense
            in blue's
                hair
            and remembers
        being
Their mother
glances over
        to
            them
and remembers
        best.

Ella Christoph, Fifth Grade
Lakeshore Elementary, San Francisco
Grace Grafton, Poet-Teacher

The Power of Feeling

I feel loneliness, a deep pain
a pain that goes on for an infinity.
I feel loneliness in a room full of people
always there yet never there
I feel loneliness for Stella, not just as a sister
for we have a friendship as bright as the sun.
We bond together.
I feel sorrow, sorrow for
my black and pure snow white cat.
I feel anxious to begin my life,
a life of fiery adventure, to begin my blossom.
I feel a confusion
I feel a deep confusion
that will never stop, like eternal fog.
I also feel a power of life.
I want to make a difference
A difference in sorrow and pain.
It is a power, a power we all have.

Renee Meisner, Fifth Grade
Point Arena Elementary, Point Arena
Karen Lewis, Poet-Teacher

Untitled

I am in Mexico.
How I grew up when I was young.
Selling stuff in busses —
junk food, etc.
and since now I had
a kind-of-like job
people knew me as the *el niño*.
People were kind to me
and bought stuff from me.
When the day was done
I'd take off my ragged clothes
and take a shower.
My two brothers
were working in the garden.
I went to bed, my blanket
ripped and torn.
I was cold and hungry
but when I was four
I went to a new place
and started all over.
May this be true,
I cannot remember.

Ebert Reyes, Fifth Grade
Sassarini Elementary, Sonoma
Arthur Dawson, Poet-Teacher

UNTITLED

The man sits, staring
into the eye of darkness.
He remembers the darkness of the past.
The empire of light
flickers in the cracked wind.
He fingers his coffee cup absentmindedly.
He is like a candle, alone
in a vast presence of blackness.
He can't think
while darkening light overlaps him.
As the depression of despair
settles in his mind,
his song sits in the yellow mist
of his eyes, waiting for him
to come to his senses.

Ashley Aguilar, Fifth Grade
Dunbar Elementary, Glen Ellen
Arthur Dawson, Poet-Teacher

MOON

Why is this legendary man standing on me?
I am me, the moon.
No Man on the Moon is going to be on me!
I am me, the moon.
With glittering stars for legs,
I am me, the moon.
With a pink-and-purple-and-blue-and-green nose that's made of
    pepperoni and olive pizza,
I am me, the moon.
With a fully decorated Christmas tree for my mouth,
I am me, the moon.
With gargantuan strawberries for ears,
I am me, the moon.
With a big pink cap eraser for a mouth,
I am me, the moon.
With pencil arms and pen hands,
I am me, the moon.
You see?
I have NO room for a man.
I AM ME, THE MOON!

Hana Kadoyama, Fifth Grade
Manor School, Fairfax
Albert DeSilver, Poet-Teacher

The Golden Apple and
the Flame of the Heart

I am the kelp
swaying in the sea
with the orange garibaldi,
the wind, the tides
I am the squash and tomatoes
in my grandfather's garden
on the shores of New Hampshire's
Lake Winnesquam
I am the smile
on my great-grandfather Chaim's face
when we went to Moscow
to see the Czar
I am the mice dreams
in my cat Brutus'
peachy apricot and cream head,
the sorbet blackberry cream violas
sitting in my mother's garden smelling like a rose
A golden apple
hanging all alone
on a light green tree
swaying, shining
on an uninhabited
silent
green mountain
dancing with the late May breezes
A hawk
gliding through the desert sky,
my red and gold feathers
rustling in the wind
smiling at the rocky red cliffs

I am the flickering orange
flame of the heart
glowing with warmth
and happiness
Suddenly
fading, dying away
until there is no flame
left.

Matthew A. White, Fifth Grade
Marquez Elementary, Los Angeles
Sita Stulberg, Poet-Teacher

UNTITLED

Sunflowers blossom as the
blind man steps out of his home.
His keys jingle in his hand.
The river of music shouts through the air.
But still as silent as a century
a current of secret birds
lingers through the vacant sky.
I feel lost but I am at home.
I remember the blind man's walk.
I remember his sleepy-looking eyes.
The blind man scares me, but without
him the sunflowers will not blossom.

Lauren Esterle, Fifth Grade
Rooftop Alternative School, San Francisco
Gail Newman, Poet-Teacher

Untitled

I.

My mom is like a barracuda
swimming around
looking for me
the baby eel
and big sister, the shark.

My mom still loves us
even when we are lost.

She will not stop looking
for us
until she finds us.

II.

I'm a sad iceberg because the mom
floated away.
I'm a tree on a hill with no nest
with chirping.
A swimming pool with no water
to swim in.
A windmill that does not
make electricity.
A leaf without
a person in sight.
A child with no voice.
A city with no echo.

Alex Martin, Fifth Grade
Ulloa Elementary, San Francisco
Susan Terence, Poet-Teacher

I Am A

I am/a computer/that flies/in the sky

I am/
a dog/
that/
bit/
the mailman/

I am a boy who/
repairs a/
man/

I am a/
school that/
likes/
spelling/

I am a girl/
who/
kills/
toys/

I am a flower that eats/
paper

I am a letter G that/
runs naked/

I am a/
whale/that/
walks in air/

Eli Ronas, Fifth Grade
Longfellow Elementary, San Francisco
Julie Gamberg, Poet-Teacher

UNTITLED

A romantic novel, refused to
publish. A life of joy
lost by a decision.
Why do I look in the mirror
and see myself standing there
with no meaning like a squirrel
staring at an old stump?

Daniel James Johengen, Fifth Grade
Rooftop Alternative School, San Francisco
Gail Newman, Poet-Teacher

VALENTINE'S DAY

My valentines have gone
to the rightful owners.
The valentines that belong
to me have come. To find
what they mean is harder
than digging through a universe
of what contains admiration,
joy and happiness. To find
the words to put them
together is like putting
a puzzle of millions of
pieces together in a day of
minutes.

Katrina Harvey, Fifth Grade
Rooftop Alternative School, San Francisco
Gail Newman, Poet-Teacher

Anger to Forgiveness

It's black
dead silent
invisible mist
no bright light penetrates
then it turns to white —
forgiveness
a long drawl
a small ripple
then a silent whirlpool.

Trevor Cushman, Fifth Grade
West Marin School, Point Reyes Station
Terri Glass, Poet-Teacher

Untitled

Damp, icy plants everywhere. Bee plants dry though
living.   Lake Merced green and blue. Foggy like
the clouds in the sky and makes you feel you've died
and a whole new life begins. The gods and
goddesses are hiding their faces behind the dark,
white, thick clouds. The fish from the old Lake
Merced are telling you, you will stay here. They are
telling you, you will swim all day and play with mud.
No I tell them.

Marianna Tischenko, Fifth Grade
Lakeshore Elementary, San Francisco
Grace Grafton, Poet-Teacher

(POEM WITH SOUND EFFECTS)

The k, h, c, g and half of B
went to ski, but they were caught
in an avalanche

"kabagchk"

z, j, v, w, s and a quarter of t
were caught in a rainstorm
once h was found and free

"sshzvwd"

Ai and e screamed
when their car was stolen

"iaeeee"

f, r, v, o and a partial L
had been caught in a wind

"oooooioooourf"

all the others are sick
now they were too.
except q
        q was in a tornado

"qqqqqq"

Hannah Moreo, Fifth Grade
Bellevue Elementary, Santa Rosa
Arthur Dawson, Poet-Teacher

Sometimes I think of what you must feel
When you see me.
It must hurt you to think of why my
parents put the block between us.
The block of the language between us.
You come outside to help me.
You in your traditional Spanish shawl and
rice-smelling dress.
Me, feeling so awkward in regular jeans
and a t-shirt.
You talk to me in a way I can understand
you most —

in love.

Though it should have been hard with
slobbery dogs jumping on us and
distracting bees buzzing loudly in our
ears.

I understood what you were trying to do
And I was happy.

Daniela Garcia, Fifth Grade
Fred Williams School, Oxnard
Shelley Savren, Poet-Teacher

Imagine a world in which there is no time. Only images.
— Alan Lightman, from *Einstein's Dreams*

The rhythmic humming of windshield wipers on a rainy day.
The silent spring of a grasshopper jumping from emerald leaf
to leaf. A rotting peach, surrounded by a mass of red ants. A
group of frozen carolers singing softly on the doorstep of a
wealthy old woman's house. Wax dripping sloppily from a
candle, a blob of brown ice cream on a recently-mopped tile
floor. A young boy ripping shreds of red and purple wrap-
ping paper all over the floor, his eyes as bright as fire. A
flowered teapot, a gold watch. A cracked peanut in search of
its shell. An old wrinkled face frowning, then smiling. A
woman holding out a slice of wheat bread for her son. A
lucky penny gleaming on the sidewalk, soon to be discovered
by a seven-year-old girl in a green and blue polka-dot dress.
An orange cat curled up on a plaid blanket in front of a
toasty fire. A maroon nail polish stain on a white carpet seat
cover. A brown button, a painting of a pear.

Katy Hill, Sixth Grade
Hall Middle School, Larkspur
Robin Jacobson, Poet-Teacher

A Piece of the World

My mother's kitchen is the world
A window to the world
We are the rice of Asia
The pizza of Italy
The fresh tacos of Mexico
The aromas of the world
Float into our noses like fireflies
In every bite a piece of the world
Come into our kitchen
Step into the world . . .

Hugh Pham, Sixth Grade
Horace Mann Middle School, San Diego
Glory Foster, Poet-Teacher

Sleepy

I know that my bed
was made
but I feel as if I want to go back.
I feel like the sloth climbing
his tree.
I feel like a crocodile who
has just climbed a mountain
                carrying stones
behind him.

Tjaden Olm, Sixth Grade
Madera Elementary, Simi Valley
Lucia Lemieux, Poet-Teacher

HARMONY

Harmony walks onto her balcony
wearing a fur-rimmed coat,
hot coals glittering bright in her hair.
Her feet are usually bare
for the cold February morning.
Leaping through the snow
she is like a restless rabbit.
At her feet rests a snow-drop
which she gently plucks and puts between her toes.
Shaking her cream-colored hair
she is not wrinkled or sunken in.
Her glassy blue eyes only look onto peace.
Her fresh red lips are usually placed in a smile
though she has a stubborn chin
and her nose tells her age is an impish nineteen.
As she passes, people call out *thanks*
for the free world.

Kirsty Lawson, Sixth Grade
Miller Creek Middle School, San Rafael
Karen Benke, Poet-Teacher

SNOW

I went up to the mountains,
An avalanche came down.

"Stop," I said.
"I will not
hurt you."

But it didn't stop —
it was a jackrabbit flying
down the slope.

The snow said,
"Why should I trust you?
You're just like the rest."

In a heartbeat,
the white slush tumbled upon me.
It thrashed me around
like an inner-tube
in the ocean.

Then
the snow felt what was inside of me,
and set me free.

Voices of the Sixth Grade
Madera Elementary, Simi Valley
Lucia Lemieux, Poet-Teacher

Untitled

Poetry
Is a flower,
A drop of color,
A glimmering light,
A patch of
Blue sky
On a cloudy day;
A song, half remembered
Now known again;
A tapestry
Woven with words.
And a poet
Is a gardener — tends the plants,
A painter — colors the world,
A flame-keeper — brightens the night,
A weather-worker — clears the skies,
A singer — loosing the words,
A weaver — crafts the cloth.
And the teacher of
Poets and poetry
Is the earth for the planting,
The brush for the paints,
The wick for the spark,
The brightness for the air,
The seeker for the tune,
The loom for the thread.
And these
Remake the world.

Lani Goto, Seventh Grade
Santa Cruz County Summer Mentorship Program
Mary Renga, Poet-Teacher

CRAZY CAT GIRL

Crazy eternal Cat Girl
Arriba
Magenta underwear
Funky chicken
Dancing to disco
Shaking her feathered tail
Crazy Cat Girl
With a bad hair day
And magenta pants
Jumping like a spazz
Is a spazz
Is a raspberry
Growing
On a blueberry bush
A purple Pizzazz Pinata
Filled with crimson frogs
And chartreuse jalapeños
Doing the macarena
The chicken dance
The chicken dancing
Macarena Jalapeño
Night club dance
Dance the night away
Fireworks tornado
Spinning
Setting Ricky Martin's
Head on fire
Vocal Spaghetti
Wrapped around a chunk
Of the sky

A piece of craziness
Lands in your pants
And makes you
Dance
A loony goony dance
Across the kitchen floor
As twilight disappears
Into dawn
Arriba
Crazy Cat Girl ...

Destini Digiorgio, Seventh Grade
Mesa Verde Middle School, San Diego
Glory Foster, Poet-Teacher

UNTITLED

I am the sun
of the San Francisco Mission District.
    I am the ruthless wind
        that blows when battle happens.
I have the wisdom and the knowledge
of the moon on the street
        Who else is the hawk in the sky?
        But me, the language
of the sudden heartbeat.
In the secret island
        in the inner city,
        the life as a garden
        is laid to rest.

Mitchell Salazar, Eighth Grade
Hanna Boys Center, Sonoma
Arthur Dawson, Poet-Teacher

Hi, My Name is Rosa Parks

All I did was sit down
and it wasn't such a good seat either
just a seat.
All I did was sit down
and keep on sitting.
So what if a white man asked for my seat?
So what?
I got here first. It's mine.
The seat is mine.
And pretty soon all Blacks were saying it
"This seat is mine."
"This seat is mine."
". . . and if you tell me otherwise,
I won't say it again.
I won't even try sitting down again."

So the white folks finally said the seat was ours.
The history books say it was me who caused it
but I don't think so
It was all of us,
and it's not fair
for me
to take all the credit.

Hi, my name is Rosa Parks
and all I did was sit down.

Helen Deng, Eighth Grade
Marina Middle School, San Francisco
Susan Terence, Poet-Teacher

INNER STRENGTH

Gone
Like the sun disappearing into the icy cold and distant mountains
Canada geese leaving their homes and flying west
Mother coyotes abandoning their dens
Hunting for food for their young

Gone
Like aqua blue caterpillars emerging from their cocoons
becoming extraordinary butterflies
Flying away
Fish swimming away from their families
Puppies separated from loved ones at birth

Gone
Like lavender tulips being picked and taken away from a
    mystical garden
Autumn leaves, bright red, shimmering orange, and soft yellow
Blowing in the wind far away from its original tree home

She is gone
The inspiration of my life
The one who laughed with me
Cried with me
Lighting up the room
Bright green hazel eyes
Radiant as a crackling fire
Expressing my deepest secrets

She is gone
Yet, I don't choke with pain
Nor sob
I don't weep with anguish
or cry myself to sleep

She is gone
Soups are tasteless
Shrieks of laughter are painful to my ears
Love is unheard of
I am numb
Knives can pierce my bare flesh
I would feel nothing

Gone
Hazel eyes no more
Consumed by the treacherous disease of Cancer
Spirit lifting from the earth
Drifting into other worlds
Yet remaining my inner strength
Guiding me through life forever

Michele Goldman, Eighth Grade
Temple Emanuel Community Day School, Los Angeles
Sita Stulberg, Poet-Teacher

THE SPOILING OF AN AGING KIWI

His body old and soft to the touch
the color of his skin grayish-brown
his wooden rocking chair creaks as
he rocks back and forth
shedding small, black hairs
on the seat.
His arms and legs sprout
small, curly black hairs that tickle
as they brush against your skin.
He has long hairy toes
hair coming out of his ears, his nostrils
he's quiet and speaks little.

In his eyes I see a lively waterfall
with rocks on its banks covered in green moss
once a bright vibrant thing
rich, ripe, and vigorous in his youth
now he grows near
to rotting in the earth
— grows dry.

Now I must leave him alone
must let him be
must let the spoiling of age
swallow him whole
and spit out the pit
that was once his soul.

Alegria Vicencio, Eighth Grade
Bonita Vista, San Diego
Johnnierenee Nelson, Poet-Teacher

UNTITLED

I come from "home"
from "that place"
The place where you can't have two children
          in one family
because then the country will explode
I come from here
from my family that says
"I'll be there for you" but isn't
I come from "listen to me" and "don't talk"
I come from Mom and Dad who love me
and want the best for me
although I don't know it.
I come from my sister
"the good" or "bad" influence
depending on her mood.
I come from a flat with ten people on the same floor,
from days when I come home and they're all there
"to greet me" so they say.
I come from plain white rice, alligator soup,
and other "delicacies."
I come from the red, white, and blue
where I drink too much Pepsi and not enough tea.

Helen Deng, Eighth Grade
Marina Middle School, San Francisco
Susan Terence, Poet-Teacher

A POEM

I am the toys that you have forgotten,
I am the dark before the light,
I am the wrapper of a candy long eaten,
I am the friend that only you were able to see,
I am the dreams not quite remembered,
I am the oyster fishermen cast aside in search of a pearl,
I am the dirt, in which a flower may grow,
I am the pages on which a story is written,
I am your shadow, who will always be with you.

William Chan, Ninth Grade
Lowell High, San Francisco
Susan Terence, Poet-Teacher

SOJOURNER TRUTH

A lightning bolt upon her creator's word,
A mudslide through the nation for her people,
A tank on the enemy's territory.

Rose above oppression,
No more bruises upon her body,
No more tears in her eyes.

A pawn into a queen,
Flint into fire,
A revolution.

Nico Gallyot, Eighth Grade
Marina Middle School, San Francisco
Susan Terence, Poet-Teacher

Why do we hide from the rain?
Why do the clouds howl?
When the wind blows, who blows it?
Is thunder the bully of the rain?
My voice is high-spirited and calm like an angel's touch.

Do you miss writing plays and sonnets?
What do you do all day?
Do you watch over us?
Do you miss the smell of air?
Do you miss your body?
What would you do differently if you had a second chance?
Would you have liked to stay or leave?
It was not my decision to leave.

What are your reasons for being mad?
Why do people waste their energy on being angry?
Why does pain hurt so badly?
Does suffering ever suffer?
What is the meaning of being lonely?
When you're upset, where does your happiness go?
Can your heart ache for someone you hate?
Are tears salty because your heart's sour?
I am laid to rest with honor, the smell of air is not missed
for I would breathe the very air of all races and that is
   disgusting.

How can an igloo keep you warm?
How does a person learn to love?
My fire died only to burn higher in the sky.

Do mirages migrate?
Does smiling mean you're truly happy?
Why is hidden beauty hidden from the weak?
Why are there so many types of one art?
Why do we have religion?
At night I rest on the curve of the crescent moon.

How did things change as you became an adult?
Did you give your life the best of you?
Will you wait for me?
Where do babies come from?
Unknown, she died when she was only seven days old.

Why do we care?

Voices of the Ninth Grade
Hoover High School, San Diego
minerva, Poet-Teacher

POEM

I'm not trying to say horses aren't a miracle
I'm not trying to say whales don't lie
I'm not trying to say love leads to loneliness
I'm not trying to say almonds are orange
I'm not trying to say girls are luckier than boys
I'm not trying to say ghosts can keep secrets
And I'm sure not trying to say poetry is easy
Because it's not.

Tashira Miggins, Tenth Grade
Sobriety High School, Marin County
Prartho Sereno, Poet-Teacher

JUNGLE JANE = HERO

A jungle of cabinets
Untamed oil in the heart
of a frying pan
Heat of a volcano
in the mouth of a stove
Mom at the center of chaos ...
Unflinchingly taming the oil
happily befriending the stove
All without lifting a spatula ...

Jenilee Quinto, Tenth Grade
Morse High School, San Diego
Glory Foster, Poet-Teacher

THINGS WILL GET BETTER

I feel great
I feel stable
I feel alone in my ways
I can feel the anger filling the room
as He walks down the steps
I hear His voice before he speaks
I feel the helplessness before he comes
I hear my door open before he opens it
I see him in front of me before he's present
I hear his sharp voice, "things will get better"
the words he spoke to me before the beginning
of time.
The words of love filled with hate

I stand there with a blanked look
Trying to stand perfectly, trying not to cause
even more hatred. Trying not to look challenging.
But yet even my presence is challenging to him.
I take off my hat, I stand limp, I take off my fake smile,
I take off my shoes to make myself small;
I find myself looking like the helpless boy I try not to be.
But yet his hatred is no challenge for my helplessness.
I realize I made a mistake somewhere in my perfection
in his eyes. For yes there's a wrinkle in the sheets of my bed,
yes there's a crumb on my lip, I didn't put the
toilet seat down, I folded his clothes
wrong, I ate too much. I look into
the eyes of my ruler and realize I
did everything right in all the wrong
ways. For I did wash the car, I did
clean his room, I did do his laundry
I did do the dishes, I did rake the leaves,
and all I did perfect, but that doesn't matter
as his words run in a blur.
I want to hide but I can't because I'm exposed
I want to run but I may hit a wall and fall.
I feel his power overcome me.
I feel nothing as I fall to the ground.
I knew this would happen before he came.
I knew it would happen when I laughed
as I put the toilet seat up, and wet the floor
I see now that things will
get better.

Robby Montgomery, Tenth Grade
YES High School, Santa Cruz
Kim Nelson, Poet-Teacher

POEM

What are in those puddles after a rain?
Do they capture images and hold them there,
bound with soaked yellow leaves? And —
what happens when the puddles disappear?
The leaves remain, a bit dilapidated, but what
about . . .? Shall I even say it?
Is the mud a keeper of dreams? Are they lost
there somewhere, is this where they belong?
When I go to the creek by the mud, why
doesn't it laugh at me? Don't I look pathetic
enough? Can it taste my tears, hold them,
keep them? Can I take my sadness back,
throw it in the water, let it float away
like two ants in bath water
whirling down the drain? Is there a chance
it could come back?

Amanda Variz, Eleventh Grade
De Anza High School, Richmond
Maureen Kerl DiSavino, Poet-Teacher

BEACH WITHIN A SHELL

Grainy dust in your crevices
can't be reached no matter how hard I try
with my damp, crumpled Kleenex
that has been carelessly strewn on the desk too long.
You have trapped splashy rays from the white sun
and they dull your purple, trying to break free.
But I see the profile of a closed sideways eye
tenderly painted in purple on your brightest spot.
You look asleep.

Angry, jagged edges, ignored by the lashing of the
smoothing waves,
scrape my dry skin
remind me that you are not all smooth pearl.
The sea has tumbled about you
like twirling blue gymnasts
in a weeping whirlpool.
You are safe in my home.
Will you ever open your one eye?
Or has the bitter salt from the ocean blinded you so?

You'll remember me from your corner of the shelf
but right now, you watch me with your closed eye
and I will one day drown in your shadow.

Faith Lin, Eleventh Grade
La Jolla High, La Jolla
Jill Moses, Poet-Teacher

EMPTY

The wind blew through me
like black knotted fish bones
beneath an oil lamp.
The raven's orange moon
choking on its own white feathers
failed to catch me
and I lost myself.
The rain tasted of moss
and soap.
Why doesn't anyone tell me these things?
How could I see that
cloudless indigo banana leaves
taste sweeter under the cold north star?
The twenty rows of mango trees
strain and wheeze, unable to explain
that in the clouds the snow sees its soul,
that, on the wall, the top hat I'd forgotten
is hanging itself.
I see too late
the octopus of time
knotting its arms outside the window.

Sarah Lambert, Eleventh Grade
La Jolla High, La Jolla
Jill Moses, Poet-Teacher

She Was

She was around the hood
with her shorts and small
black top, copper skin and shiny black
hair, eyes as wide as a bus light,
had no idea
the boys on the block wanted to
get in her lil shorts.

A desert vulture man comin
down from the rich hills, comin
from behind with his white hat,
cane and gold chain.

No one knew him, his face
was blurry like a runny egg.

He grabbed her by her hair
and pulled her like a rope
around a dog's neck
and held.

The sky cried and moaned
that day, the gutters wet and red
as a bottle of Passion Alzay.

April O'Neal, Eleventh Grade
Stronghold, Canby
Stephen Torre, Poet-Teacher

WINTER LANDSCAPE

My sister is the winter moon
She eclipses the sun with her soft white light
She guides me through the crumbling moss of nightmares

My sister smells like the mist of canyons
She laughs like the light that floods a greenhouse atrium
She cries like shadows in a field filled with sharp grass
Her hair is black seaweed that
Tangos in the rough waves of the ocean

Crossing the brilliant white wilderness
She leaves her footprints in the wet snow
Sepia-colored memories fill my hands
And sift through my fingers like grains of sand

But light can travel even across empty space
"I see the moon, and the moon sees me"
In a dimension where yesterday and today embrace each other
Sometimes the moon rises in the morning
Sometimes the moon swims inside the sea

As the gentle clouds melt into the solitary sky
Together we watch the universe accelerate
At the speed of leaves falling off poplar trees

Masumi Taketomi, Eleventh Grade
La Jolla High, La Jolla
Jill Moses, Poet-Teacher

MEMORY STAIN

If I loosened its grip on my
emotional jugular
I might be rid of a thin track
of pale skin, like a crop circle
tainted on the flesh that
paints my voice box
a silver sliver of two hours of
memories, worth something
bigger than I can name
hanging by a cheap dime-colored chain
from where I draw my fire
need it so badly like a
shot to the heart.

Gina Abelkop, Eleventh Grade
La Jolla High, La Jolla
Jill Moses, Poet-Teacher

WHY DO WE SLIP?

We drink to get ova
we smoke to get high
try to keep our composure
have a good alibi
we fight we ain't shy
we jack cause we ready
to ride
we ride cause we think
we are ready to die
but we don't know why.

Barbara Barnes, Eleventh Grade
Stronghold, Canby
Stephen Torre, Poet-Teacher

A Poem for My Dad

If I were to write a poem for my dad
    I wouldn't

I'd leave a blank line for every night he came home late

I'd write a line about how supportive he's been
    then I'd erase it

I'd leave some blank space for each of his
    unfulfilled expectations

I'd have to turn the page over
    the first side would be full
    of empty lines

On the back I'd write a list of things I've done
    Won A+ first place

I'd staple another sheet on top
    so he can see the list of things I've done
    that count

I'd leave it blank too

I'd leave a line unwritten
    for every time he made Ima cry

A smudge of ink
    for every time he stayed silent
    avoiding understanding
    her tears
    would darken my paper

I'd write a poem for my dad
    using all the pencils he's given me
    with no strings attached

It would be very short

Liat Gat, Twelfth Grade
Palo Alto High School, Palo Alto
Mary Lee McNeal & Nancy Mohr, Poet-Teachers

OUR ALPHABET

A is a mountain with lots of snow on top, a long road with a
   tree across it, a king's crown, the tip of a rocket, the head of
   a bullet.
B is number 13 squeezed together, two brass knuckles.
C is a horseshoe, is an earlobe.
D is a golf club, half a moon, a belly, a cup handle, a baby in the
   bag, something half-round and broken.
E is a backward number 3, an ear, a cup handle.
F is a toothbrush with no bristles.
G is the crescent moon with a man sitting on it.
H is two people on different tracks that finally come together,
   an "I" on its side, a hill, a broken chair.
I is a scarecrow, and H lying down, an upside-down exclamation
   point, a short line.
J is a fishhook under water, upside down 2.
K is a sawhorse, a person leaning against the wall.
L is a stick, a right angle, a bed.
M is a fish-mouth, the Twin Peaks, a butt.
N is an elbow on a table.
O is the sun, a donut, the number zero, a circle, the clear white
   eyeball, a fruit.
P is a sword, a flag for peace.
Q is a blunt sitting in an ashtray, a bowl with a spoon in it, an
   upside down cherry,   a musical note, some big thing.
R is the number 12 squished together.
S is bike marks, a curvy street, Lombard St., a snake.
T is an intersection, a cross, a table with one leg.
U is somebody's tongue sticking out, a U-turn.
V is a nose, an arrow pointing south, an ice cream cone that's
   empty.

W is a woman's breasts, an upside down M, the top of an
   alien's head.
X is a four-way entrance to a middle, a railroad track crossing,
   two intersecting lines, the two-way road.
Y is a tree branch.
Z is a zig-zag street.

**Myron Bridges, James Crawford, Travette Crawford,
Selvin Guevara, Sara Hernandez, Antonio Lopez,
Demond Norman, Leonard Ram, Geronal Washington,
Alfonso Zamora**
*SF Conservation Corps/California Charter Academy, San
Francisco*
Andrea Ross, Poet-Teacher

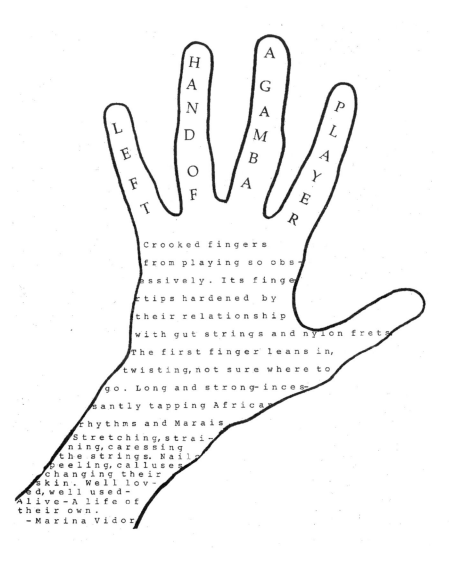

L E F T
H A N D O F
A G A M B A
P L A Y E R

Crooked fingers
from playing so obs-
essively. Its finge
rtips hardened by
their relationship
with gut strings and nylon frets
The first finger leans in,
twisting, not sure where to
go. Long and strong-inces-
santly tapping Africa
rhythms and Marais
Stretching, strai-
ning, caressing
the strings. Nail
peeling, calluses
changing their
skin. Well lov-
ed, well used-
Alive-A life of
their own.
-Marina Vidor

Marina Vidor, Twelfth Grade
Palo Alto High School, Palo Alto
Mary Lee McNeal & Nancy Mohr, Poet-Teachers

POET/TEACHER POEMS

THE WOMEN HAVE ALL GONE

The pile of sand outside
shifts against the house.
He is startled and sits up
to the wind like his wife
in childbirth. He hates
the curl falling over his eye
so he reaches to the night-
stand for the vodka he fell
asleep to, when the handle
of the door turns, he lies
down whispering, "The drink
is for my cold, and she
is the last thing on my mind."

Marcielle Brandler
Pasadena

ARIADNE'S THREAD

Like a spider's fragile labrynth,
the lines crisscrossing our palms
are visible portions of a huge web
which not only connects all of us, but
contains leaf veins and leopard claws as well.
— from *Alphabet Naturae*, by Vitus Bremeyev

He leaves her standing
on the threshold. Her face
setting like a full moon
behind the iron door.

Everything goes black.
His eyes grope for an image,
then wither and retreat inward
like twin raindrops on a face of stone.

Reluctantly, his fingers
take up the body's lamp,
knowing that safe passage
depends on the most delicate act:

finding a spider's thread
and following it
hand under hand
through the dark.

Slowly
he learns the gestures
demanded of the blind.
Suspended

between fear and desire,
he discovers a way forward,
commits himself to a path
too thin to walk.

Arthur Dawson
San Francisco

GREAT JOY DAWN, MAY 25

Haus St. Benedict, Wurzburg

After two hour's sleep I wake to laughter
    too carefree for death —
a band of blond Angels delicately tickling
    the tar off my heart with their tongues
        as if it were honey.

My room is dark   I am light.
I give light. Everything around me shines.
Holy lascivious outlaw mysteries tremble
coursings of divine rapture.   I was right
to desire what no one could give.
I neither defile nor betray, rather I cherish
    and somehow hang on, submitting
to such indignities the Goddess left
her sanctuary to enter me as Peace
    passing all understanding. Shanti.
Flying would not take me higher
"You see what love has done to me"
look! look! Everything around me shines.
The Angels kissed me in the darkness —
Now I shine.

Will Staple
Nevada City

THINKING OF SAINT FRANCIS

They say he spoke with animals.
The say he touched the birds.
That birds came to him and sat in his hand.
For myself, I've always wanted that.
Belief.

Outside our house a blue jay makes her nest.
Three or four baby birds,
all squawks and beaks.
I can't see them yet.
So like a prayer
I imagine them in their fullness later.

In the morning she brings a green berry for them to share.
Suddenly she looks so small against the rest of nature.
But she is quite fierce really.
Protecting them.
Using her voice,
even against the orange cat.

It's all we've got.
Our voice.
Words like home and here and peace.
This moment.
Love and loyalty.
Belief.

Mary Renga
Mt. Shasta

AFTER SCHOOL

The boy from third grade takes the sidewalk home
His back pack hangs over one shoulder
Clouds turning a space, the sky opening around him
Rounding the corner
His thoughts fly into blue.

Wind, wind, wind, white cloud —
He chants the wing-beat rhythm, a game
He still plays
Earlier during Poetry he was caught
Again the teacher called on him, asking
What he wants most are wings, he answered.

Like the red-tailed hawk's he watches
Circling the roof of his house, circling
Like time if only it could move backward
Back when his parents were together.

Together he will fold the halves of paper
Carefully, white over white
Folding, re-folding, a paper airplane
In his room above the garage
His window overlooking the backyard
He sits there imagining, he can fly
Far away, watching
The hawks soar over the lawns, the houses
His thoughts circling today, tomorrow —
Nobody home but me.

Karen Benke
Mill Valley

GRIEF

Once again grief visited me
in the middle of the night.
Knocking down the already tattered door,
it moved in like a hurricane
ripping the tightly tucked-in sheets
from the bedframe,
scattering letters that were neatly stacked
on the secretary's desk
and the candlelight flicker on the wall
so perfect in pattern
went out.
And my heart, oh my heart
was tossed around like a moon
with no gravity
and I asked Grief,
"Please put these things back
where they belong."
Grief laughed and said,
"Better get used to it,
I live here now."

Terri Glass
Greenbrae

BEN LOMOND

crickets scratch their legs together
as tree frogs call in the moon
and my daughter lies covered in sweat
golden and polished she blends in
with the oiled redwood walls, still
i cannot see her breath soft between
arms thrown wide against the bed
mouth cracked silent
she heals herself

devorah major
san francisco

W/ My Sony Walkman

I travelled
in the lowlands of Kenya
while listening to wooden sticks
tapping hollow logs
and flutes gliding softly
over green palm leaves
I walked
in a calm forest
not unknown to thunder.

Suddenly a bird chirped alone
and was echoed by a whole flock
singing up the sun
singing it over the hill
singing so shrill
while palm fronded animals began to creep
in the shadows
and the day started bright and warm.

The temperature peaked and the air
was moist in the jungle.
I lost my bearings
in the lowlands of Kenya
leafy, shadowy, dense
wondering if I was
chirping bird
gliding snake
or spotted cheetah sprinting
through the yawning trees.

Giovanna Capone
Oakland

ALICE ON THE CLOTHESLINE

*From a 1920 photograph of my grandmother, seated
across the wires of a clothesline ...*

Alice balances on the clothesline
Heels locked, hair bobbed.

She commands earth, air
she herself is fire
and with one hand
She holds off the clouds promising rain.
Her smile trumpets her wild swan nature
the thunder of her knowings
pins me to this frame.
She, legs crossed, on the clothesline
as if balancing on the bow
of a planetary viola.
She, who can fly like the snow owl over White pines.
Forty years later, I meet her,
the woman who sits on the clothesline names me,
on that hot August midnight she
collects words from the ancestors and conjures my name,
and I know her to balance above silver thimbles, wooden
spools of
black thread, Mason jars of yellow waxbeans, corn, beet
pickles,
beeswax, setting onions,
offering me sugar cookies shaped like stars
and strawberry jello in pale green tupperware,
Norwegian words and foxglove.
She floats amid cattails, Canadian geese, Russet potatoes,
wild
rice and surplus peanut butter.
Her smile revealing her wild swan nature
and her constant conversations with the moon.
A euphoria of orchids
slightly, off the ground.

JoNelle Toriseva
Berkeley

Dinosaur

I can feel the sadness of the large head
that floats in the museum like a planet

the metronome of feet shuffling past
a little sun powdering the lifted dust   and it's *halloed*

Weeks,   years,   knees
Red-raw in the dung dirt

A scientist dug you free and spelt you out for your new skin

Now the dinosaur contains what we imagined it could
A life that's visible we can reconstruct

And all these people shuffling past
Faith or what church do *you* believe in

What's behind the glass behind the skin of this life as we
pass

I am an alphabet of bones,
My own telling.

Iris Jamahl Johnson
Santa Rosa

The Other Poem

for JJ

I know you wish I had written
the other poem,
the one that wears nothing
but gypsy dresses and never
cuts her hair,
the one that acts as if
there were only the month of June
to muddle through, the one
that lives in a cabaña in Africa
and always has plenty to drink.

Perhaps if I worked at it
I could train a poem
to play the harp
or serve tea
when the afternoon wears thin.

But you may never
come across that poem;
rumor has it she lost her way
in a snowstorm one January,
spun out on a piece of black ice
and has been spinning
toward another galaxy
ever since.

Prartho Sereno
San Rafael

Joy Farm

Oh to be 14, to sign up for the horse show
when you don't even know how to ride
because your best friend wants to share this joy,
wants to pull you into the ring to feel the power
of circles. Secretly you love horses
as much as she, maybe more, driving to the country
on as many Saturdays as possible, breathing in
the wealth of clover and mown hay that releases
inhibition. You imagine yourself riding wildly across
the uninterrupted sea of brown, spring's head
not yet appeared, you and your horse almost
the only living thing. Your job is to brush
the body of your friend's horse to glisten,
after she rides, which you are happy for,
smelling its must, stroking each muscle
as if some future dream, your pony-tailed self
reflected in the dark lake of its seeing.

The day your friend wins a blue ribbon
for her skill, she says there's a place for you
in the horse show, "Novelty Class,"
and you know what you will do, tape a toy arrow
to your back, spill catsup down the point
of contact and ride the horse backwards,
groaning, an old cowboy hat on your head.
You know how to get a laugh. You know how
to make up for skill. The horse, best of all,
plays along, snorting and whinnying
at this goofy teenager who doesn't know all
she thinks, flopped on his hide making noises
it has never heard with its civil upbringing.
Confused, it reverses and high-steps
around the ring, the back becoming front
after all, its yellow teeth shining in the light,
the audience clapping their heads off.

Perie Longo
Santa Barbara

The Heart of Algebra

This week I see
my heart
is more important
than algebra or
geometry

But my teacher tells
me that math
is everything:

how many cells in
our fingers

how everything
is a story
of variables &
outcome

how the dark
days correspond
with the shades
of my heart

how music is
sweeter when
laced with
your questions

How do you
finance the life
of an artist

How do you carve
home in a
place that is
　　　not

How much does
a heart weigh when
        it's content or
                dejected

Or how does the sun
put its colors in
your hair and smile

And how does
the juxtaposition
        of sun
            &
the cold & far
            planets
bring me to this
            chair
in this room?

Maybe Mathematics
makes for a
sharper eye
so you know
when to rock
& lift us
& tell us
math will
        solve
everything:

heart or
    no heart.

Susan Terence
San Francisco

Though the poppy closes at night,
under the sun it speaks out loud,
joyous mouth, fully-lashed eye.
It does not need to think
about what it says, speech
springs from its roots right up
into the cup. Anything so orange
possesses voice. You want to know
what it says. "Day, day, day,"
is one, "slide right in," another,
"dream" a third, "dream a hammock
jugband, mango-flesh place,"
where amber holds, jelled
just this side of history, NOW
in a scent that strengthens the heart.

Grace Marie Grafton
San Francisco

LESSON PLANS
& ESSAY

SURPRISED BY LINES

Imagine thirty students, each on their individually chosen small but complete pieces of ground. The silence deepens so that bird song sounds loud. Cars murmur in the background. Asked to be alone and silent, to see, to hear, to smell, to touch, to study the nature that is available to them, they travel into a newly discovered place to find metaphors, similes, and to wait for that one new idea to be born into a poem. True, there are those who resist the silence and want to chatter together. With encouragement, they soon relax into the moment. These quiet studies of nature are the arrival point. If a poem is born, that gift is welcome. But supposing that for the first time nature is seen to be a world of surprises: tiny, minute, and always new, then that is enough. The following lesson uses this silence to release students to explore their inner selves.

A poet can usually point to a defining moment when a poem leads the poet into a new world of words. For me that discovery came in high school when I decided to do a paper on the Welsh poet Dylan Thomas. In his poetry, I felt like an explorer confronted with a landscape familiar yet charged with difference, a world lived in, looked at, but never truly *seen* before. Why not introduce students to that place where new ideas fell like a shaft of sudden sun on a stormy day? Dylan Thomas challenges his readers to let go of the rules of grammar that corral our language behind well-constructed fences.

I use this lesson at the end of a ten session residency. For weeks, students have heard about active verbs — *plunge*, not *plunging* or *is plunging*. With Thomas, verbs and nouns appear again but they're all turned around. The students follow the poem as I read for them one stanza at a time this shortened version of "Poem in October," written near the end of Thomas' life. I include the definitions of some of the more obscure words.

POEM IN OCTOBER

It was my thirtieth year to heaven
Woke to my hearing from harbour and neighbor wood
And the mussel pooled and the heron
Priested shore
The morning beckon
With water praying and call of seagull and rook*
And the knock of sailing boats on the net webbed wall
Myself to set foot
That second
In the still sleeping town and set forth.

My birthday began with the water-
Birds and the birds of the winged trees flying my name
Above the farms and the white horses
And I rose
In rainy autumn
And walked abroad in a shower of all my days.

High tide and the heron dived when I took the road
Over the border
And the gates
Of the town closed as the town awoke ...

Here were fond climates and sweet singers suddenly
Come in the morning where I wandered and listened
To the rain wringing
Wind blow cold
In the wood faraway under me ...

It turned away from the blithe country
And down the other air and the blue altered sky
Steamed again a wonder of summer
With apples
Pears and red currants
And I saw in the turning so clearly a child's
Forgotten mornings when he walked with his mother

Through the parables**
            of sun light
And the legends of the green chapels

And the twice told fields of infancy
That his tears burned my cheeks and his heart moved in mine . . .
            It was my thirtieth
Year to heaven stood there then in the summer noon...
            O may my heart's truth
                        Still be sung
On this high hill in a year's turning.

* A bird something like a crow.
** A simple story illustrating a moral or religious lesson.

At the end of each stanza, we look for new uses of words. Discovery follows discovery: *thirty years to heaven* instead of just *thirty years old. Pooled* and *priested* are nouns that become adjectives. Students' love of having the right answer leads to quite a competition as each student looks for new word uses and unusual placement of words. What an unusual way to celebrate a birthday with *birds of the winged trees flying my name.* The adverb *wringing* surprises us when it is used instead of rain *falls.* Then comes the turn of the poem: *but the weather turned around.* This phrase leads the poet down the path of memory to a simpler time when as a child he lived in the *parables of sun light* instead of in a world where war clouds the days. At the end of my reading, I ask the students to share what they have learned about the poet from reading this section of "Poem in October."

Before going outside to write, we name nouns, then use them as verbs or adjectives. We create lines like *my childhood booked me into writing.* For the students, verbs as nouns is easier. *The chase of trees, the sway of birds, they are no more.* For the assignment, I don't insist that nouns be verbs or verbs be nouns, I simply encourage the students to talk about memories or to create vivid word pictures while trying to use language in new ways, or to simply turn their poems loose and let their images surprise them. This is my last chance to remind them that the poet doesn't need to know where the poem is going. What a delight to surprise yourself as well as your reader! For much of their lives as students, they have to plan ahead and march to a logical conclusion. I choose the following two poems to illustrate the exercise, because they surprised their writers as well as their readers.

emptiness

emptiness of people
no one nothing
halls empty
streets empty
buildings empty
this makes my soul empty
my heart empty
my body empty
I am alone
me, my pencil
my paper
I am alone
no one there

still float stop go
there is no up there
is no down there are
no cities there are no
towns yet i'm stuck
in a fake world
no time no clock
there are no mountains
there are no rocks yet
i'm stuck there
is no punctuation
there are no lines
but yet i'm stuck

A.J. Wiley, Fifth grade

Trapped

I'm trapped between two
parallel lines, no way out.
I'm trapped forever.
Somehow, I don't feel
bad. The music of other
happy things comforts me.
Just think,
to us music,
to them words.

Vlad Popescu, Fifth grade

For me, the best part of being a poet-teacher lies in the thrill of showing students how to leap into new ways of thinking. When students express the freedom they feel when they let go of their minds as the controlling instrument of their poetry, I know I can warm myself in the memory of those images that stretch into another dimension of language.

— *Janice De Ruiter, Castro Valley*

The Importance of a Mentor

It was 1982 when I first encountered Robert Bly at a poetry reading in Seattle. I was struck by his flamboyant delivery even though he spoke through an annoying Mid-Western nasal tone. He accompanied himself on a dulcimer, read other poets' work as well as his own, and read or recited poems often twice, which made him stand out as a unique figure on the contemporary American poetry scene. He was as bold as the vest he wore, as controversial as his madcap white hair, and he was reaching a far greater audience than any university poet. His reading was evocative, entrancing, and thoroughly entertaining, and he had me hooked.

Bly has been influential to me in many ways. His book, *Leaping Poetry* (1975), with examples of the Spanish sensualist poets, gave me permission to make wild associations in my own poetry. I was intrigued by images that came up from deep in the unconscious and were brought to light by another leaping image. Bly's *The Morning Glory* gave rise to the form of the prose poem, a form I have experimented with and love to have the freedom to use when verse seems too constricting.

Bly has not only been instrumental in my writing, but my teaching as well. I use examples of his poems when I teach imagery and metaphor to children. There is a prose poem called "The Caterpillar," which I use as an example of good detailed imagery. I read this poem aloud to students and have them draw what they hear. I tell them that if the image can be translated as a mental picture, then the image is working. When I teach metaphor, I read another prose poem of Bly's called "The Dead Seal Near McClure's Beach." I have the students follow along on a printed copy and underline all the metaphors and similes they find embedded in it.

There are many things I admire about Robert Bly's life and work that have made his own poetry very rich: his willingness to explore the human shadow through myth and fairy tale, his politically-active stance against the war in Viet Nam, and his deep involvement with the men's movement. He constantly examines the health of our culture through his writing, as seen in one of his more recent books, *The Sibling Society*. It seems to me that Bly has achieved what Neruda said, "A poet must maintain a balance between solitude and solidarity, between feeling and action, between intimacy of mankind and the revelation of nature." And what I deeply respect Bly for is bringing many great poets from other cultures into the spotlight through his brilliant translations. I had never heard of Rilke or Rumi or Machado until Robert Bly gave them an equal voice at his readings.

Many years ago I was very discouraged with the progress of my own writing. The hatchet-method of formal poetry workshops lost its appeal as a way for me to go deeper into my writing. I was in search of a mentor and asked three poets whom I admired if they would assist me in the process. Out of those three, Robert Bly responded. After I sent him my book, he told me my poems were clear, lively, well-written, but he wanted me to delve deeper into my dark side. I sent him what I felt were dark poems, but he replied, "I don't see the dark side in a felt way, rather a witty, intellectualizing about it." Even though this was criticism, I felt honored that he thought I had wit. I sent him more poems. He wanted me to get more detailed about my objects, "Kiss each object one by one," he said. I sent him more poems. He responded, "You're a big hider." That was the last of his comments about my work over a period of four months. What his brief correspondence did give me was enough incentive to carry on, and my poetry has become more full of sensory detail and more heartfelt because of it.

When CPITS poet-teachers show young people the art of poetry, we are their mentors. Mentoring is not only teaching craft, but inspiring children to go further into their imaginations, to experiment, to be empathic with themselves and with others. Although not all of our hair is white and most of us have a way to go before we can claim that wisdom cap, we may be the children's first nudge of encouragement to become poets.

— *Terri Glass, Greenbrae*

The Heart of Courage

I begin this lesson by writing "Corazon" on the blackboard, asking if any students speak Spanish and if they can tell us what it means, which of course is "heart." I talk about how many English and Spanish words have common roots and put "core" on the board and ask for a definition of that English word and why it's similar to corazon. Another word that's spelled slightly differently but comes from the same root is "COURAGE," which I write in big letters. "What's the connection between 'courage' and 'heart?'" I ask.

Next I read Mary Oliver's "Web," (from *American Primitive*) asking the kids to listen for things she's afraid of in the poem. We get a list going on the blackboard: spiders, blood, poverty, hunger, lightning, bats, monsters in the basement, intruders (what is Oliver thinking of when she says, "the curtains move as though the wind had bones"?). From there we jump into things that the kids themselves or people in general are sometimes afraid of (some children, especially boys, won't admit to their own fears), and add to the list. I get responses like: earthquakes, cancer, being hurt, falling, speaking in public, being teased, admitting a weakness, death of a family member. Sometimes I need to dig a little — mention some of my own fears, or ask, "Is anyone here afraid of losing a family member, being made fun of, getting hurt?" etc.

Once there's a good list on the board, I mention how we often think of courage as simply being without fear, but that in fact, having courage means facing your fears. Sometimes writing a poem can be an act of courage. There's a Tibetan saying:

The first principle of a warrior is not being afraid of who you are.

Then we turn to the example poems. Often I'll start with "Stutter Stutter," explaining that Somkhit was both hard of hearing and a recent immigrant from Laos. In this poem he is talking to his stuttering as if it were a person. After reading the poem, we talk about the courage it took for Somkhit to write it. We read and discuss the other two poems, and then I give the assignment.

> Write to a fear, or a part of yourself you don't like, talking to it as if it were a person, the way Somkhit does, asking it questions. With older students I suggest including a metaphor as part of the question: "Don't just ask 'Lightning, why do you strike our houses?' But 'Why do you strike our houses like fiery swords from the sky?'" I ask students to end their poems by taking power back for themselves: "I want your teeth to turn into clay!" as one students says, or "I dream that your powerful voice will combine in mine." as Somkhit says.

Afterwards, to ensure that the students feel safe sharing their poems, I ask for a promise from that class that what gets read and said doesn't go beyond the classroom. The most moving moment I've experienced in nine years of teaching happened at the close of this lesson when one student expressed how she felt like a boy trapped in a girl's body. Almost as impressive as the student's courage was the great respect, openness, and maturity with which this intimate revelation was received by her classmates.

Stutter Stutter

Why did you make me stutter
can't you see how far I got without it?
now I'm stuck with stutter problem
and repeating life over and over.
can't you see everyone hates me
because of you?
Why did you choose me for?
Now I'm a stutter kid who's repeating
over and over don't you know why?
I hate stuttering of that silent block
of bean you gave me don't you see

I'm going through a lot of therapy
of darkness of hateness
I dream that your soul and body
of your powerful voice
will combine in mine
of sadness of stuttering.

Somkhit Thongban, Seventh grade
Hanna Boys Center, Sonoma

— Arthur Dawson, Glen Ellen

It has become widely recognized that when students begin reading, writing, and discussing poetry, they inevitably begin to appreciate the power of words, and thus begin improving in their school work. Proponents of the Literacy Campaign throughout the United States have documented numerous instances which attest to this fact.

As a poet, I have experienced another dimension to this phenomenon — a greater spiritual awareness — an empathy which can and does change lives. In many of my poetry workshops, I read a Langston Hughes poem called "Mother and Son," in which the mother warns her son that "This life ain't no crystal stair." The tragedy so eloquently expressed in just a few words is spoken by a black servant woman who is scrubbing the stairway as her son passes by. She knows that she will never escape her life of servitude. She represents the entire black race.

Students often see the tears in my eyes and understand the empathy I feel for a poet long dead and a race of people — sometimes their own people. They realize that words can indeed, all by themselves, teach us about the joys and sorrows of the "other." I also share with students "Harlem Sweeties," Hughes' jazzy celebration of beautiful women in the Harlem nightclubs, how they were like candy and caused him to soar in jubilant ecstasy.

Many students are touched when I read them William Blake's "The Chimney Sweeper." In it, the poet says:

> There's little Tom Dacre, who cried when his head,
> That curled like a lamb's back was shaved, so I said,
> 'Hush, Tom! Never mind it, for when your head's bare
> You know that the soot cannot spoil your white hair.'

The poem introduces us to children as young as four years old who lived during England's Industrial Revolution: little ones who were often orphaned and forced to become chimney sweeps. Some died before their sixth birthdays of lung conditions brought on by soot inhalation.

The room grows quiet. My students hear in the words the tragedy and inevitability of dying children in another century. Students who previously did not care about anything outside themselves begin to suspect that there is more to the written word than merely writing boring essays for some distant teacher who grades and discards them. Their discussions have more depth, they begin to feel that, because their words have value, so, too, do their spirits.

During my years as a college instructor, a visiting poet to schools, and a performer of my own work, I have seen how students and audiences are touched by uplifting words. All great art, I believe, makes better people of us. When we value our words — our most elemental symbols for communication — we value the most basic and often-used method of reaching out to our fellow human beings. I know it is true that, as one religion puts it, "In the beginning was the Word, and the Word was God."

Marcielle Brandler
Pasadena

BIBLIOGRAPHY

WEB SITES

Where you can find information:
inkspot.com
For Young Writers: Market Info
www.inkspot.com/young/market/

Where you can publish students' work:
Chapbooks for Learning
www.chapbooks.com
Note: This is not an e-zine, but an on-line company that uses the technology
to publish old-fashioned books.

Cyberkids
ages 7-12
www.cyberkids.com/we/html/kids.html

Cyberteens
ages 13-19
www.cyberteens.com

Human Beams-Young Minds
ages 10-18
www.humanbeams.com/young/index.html

KidNews
all ages, but mainly elementary grades
www.kidnews.com/

KidPub
no ages specified
www.Kidpub.org/kidpub

Kids' Space
younger children
www.kids-space.org/index.html

Kidstory
all ages, not very good prose but better poetry
www.kidstory.com

MidLink Magazine
middle school and some high school
www.cs.ucf.edu/~MidLink/

The Sidewalk's End
no ages specified
www3.cybercities.com/s/sidewalk/ezine.html

Writes of Passage
12-19
www.writes.org/index.html

(Thanks to Susanna Lang for this list.)

POETRY BIBLIOGRAPHY FOR YOUNG ADULTS

Adoff, Arnold, ed. *I Am the Darker Brother: An Anthology of Modern Poems by African Americans.*

Berry, James. *When I Dance: Poems by James Berry.*

Blum, Joshua, ed. *United States of Poetry.*

Brown, Kurt, ed. *Drive, They Said: Poems about Americans and Cars.*

Carlson, Lori, ed. *Cool Salsa: Bilingual Poems.*

Carroll, Joyce and Edward Wilson, ed. *Poetry After Lunch: Poems to Read Aloud.*

Dahl, Roald. *Fractured Fairy Tales.*

Duffy, Carol Ann, ed. *I Wouldn't Thank You for a Valentine: Poems for Young Feminists.*

Dunning, Stephen, Edward Leuders, and Hugh Smith, eds. *Reflections on a Gift of Watermelon Pickle ...And Other Modern Verse* and *Some Haystacks Don't Even Have Any Needle ...And Other Complete Modern Poems.*

Fleishman, Paul. *I Am Phoenix: Poems for Two Voices.*

Fletcher, Ralph. *Room Enough for Love.*

Frost, Robert, and Peter Koeppen, illus. *A Swinger of Birches: Poems of Robert Frost for Young People.*

Giovanni, Nikki, ed. *Shimmy Shimmy Shimmy Like My Sister Kate: Looking at the Harlem Renaissance through Poems.*

Glenn, Mel. *Class Dismissed! High School Poems, Class Dismissed II, The Taking of Room 114, Jump Ball: Basketball Season,* and *Who Killed Mr. Chippendale?.*

Gordon, Ruth, ed. *Pierced by a Ray of Sun: Poems about the Times We Feel Alone,* and *Under All Silences: Shades of Love.*

Greenfield, Eloise. *Honey, I Love, and Other Love Poems.*

Hempel, Amy and Jim Shepard ed. *Unleashed: Poems by Writers' Dogs.*

Hesse, Karen. *Out of the Dust.*

Hirschfelder, Arlene B., and Beverly R. Singer, eds. *Rising Voices: Writings of Young Native Americans.*

Hull, Robert, ed. *Breaking Free: An Anthology of Human Rights Poetry.*

Johnson, James Weldon, *The Creation.*

Kerdian, David, ed. *Beat Voices: An anthology of Beat Poetry.*

Koch, Kenneth, and Kate Farrell, eds. *Talking to the Sun: An Illustrated Anthology of Poems for Young People.*

Larrick, Nancy, ed. *Bring Me All of Your Dreams.*

Livingston, Myra Cohn, ed. *A Time to Talk: Poems of Friendship*, and *Call Down the Moon: Poems of Music.*

Lyne, Sandford, ed. *Ten-Second Rainshowers: Poems by Young People.*

Marcus, Leonard S., ed. *Lifelines: A Poetry Anthology Patterned on the Stages of Life.*

Medearis, Angela Shelf. *Skin Deep, and Other Teenage Reflections.*

Merriam, Eve. *Inner City Mother Goose.*

Miller, E. Ethelbert, ed. *In Search of Color Everywhere.*

Morrison, Lillian, ed. *Rhythm Road: Poems to Move to.*

Nye, Naomi Shihab and Paul B. Janeczko, ed. *I Feel a Little Jumpy Around You.*

Nye, Naomi Shihab, ed. *This Same Sky: A Collection of Poems from Around the World.*

Peacock, Molly, Elise Paschen, Neil Neches ed. *Poetry in Motion : 100 Poems from the Subways and Buses.*

Rosenberg, Liz, ed. *The Invisible Ladder: An Anthology of Contemporary American Poems for Young Readers.*

Try these websites for other poetry bibliographies:.
www.clpgh.org/ein/ya/yapoetry.html.
www.nypl.org/branch/teen/earth.html.

(Compiled by Maureen Kerl DiSavino)

Dear Students-Poets,.

Here are some magazines that accept children's finished poems — poems that you have rewritten, typed out, and properly spelled and checked over. Send your best work. When you send your poems to a magazine, remember:

1. Include a cover sheet with your name and home address and phone number; your grade, school, school address, and phone number; and teacher's name if appropriate;

2. Send a self-addressed, stamped envelope (SASE) that's big enough and has enough postage, so that the editors can return your work if they don't choose to use it. Don't be discouraged! Many writers get rejection slips, even your own poet-teachers;

3. Type your full name, address, school, and age on each poem. If your poem is more than one page, put this information on each page;

4. Be patient. Good luck! Keep trying! Keep writing!

Children's Digest, Box 567 Indianapolis, IN 46206. Publishes eight times a year. Requires a letter from your parent or teacher stating that the work is originial. Payment in copies and special subscription rate. Prints about 30 poems per year. Send SASE. Responds in eight to ten weeks. Editor's advice: Keep trying!

Creative Kids, Box 6448 Mobile, AL 36660. Publishes eight times a year, ages 5-18. Each piece must be labeled with the student's name, birth date, address, and school address. Responds in four weeks, pays in free magazine. A recent school picture is a good idea. Sometimes an accepted work will take a long time to get into print, depending on the theme of your poem. Editor's advice: Keep trying!.

Highlights for Children, 803 Church St. Honesdale, PA 18431. Publishes 11 times a year, prints 10 to 15 poems per issue. Also publishes adult articles. Tries to respond in four weeks. Grades K-12. Put your age on the poems along with your name and address.

Merlyn's Pen, PO Box 1058, East Greenwich, CT 02818. Publishes four times a year. Accepts all forms of writing and artwork from students in grades 7-12. Cover sheet and SASE required. Responds to all submissions, usually within ten weeks. Payment: three copies of the magazine.

Stone Soup, The Magazine for Children, Children's Art Foundation, Box 83, Santa Cruz, CA 95063. Publishes five times a year. Accepts poems, stories, artwork, and book reviews by children. Age limit: 13. Responding time: four weeks. payment in copies and cash. Editor's advice: read a few issues to find out if your work is suitable for the magazine. Send a SASE.

CLASSIC TEXTS ABOUT TEACHING POETRY AND POETRY WRITING TO CHILDREN

Children Write Poetry:A Creative Approach, 1951, 1967, Flora J.Arnstein, Dover Books.

Creative Power, Hughes Mearnes, 1929, Dover Books.

Getting From Here to There:Writing and Reading Poetry, Florence Grossman, Boynton/Cook Publishers.

Sound and Sense:An Introduction to Poetry, 1956, Laurence Peffine, Harcourt Brace Jovanovich.

Wishes, Lies, and Dreams, 1970, and *Rose, Where Did You Get That Red?*, 1973, Kenneth Koch, Vintage Books, Random House.

RECOMMENDED TEXTS

The Art of Writing:A Guide for Poets, Students, and Readers, by William Packard, St. Martin's Press, NY © 1992. Karl Shapiro writes that this is a classic among poetry writing how-to books. It includes not only the history of poetry and poetic devices, but writing challenges to develop form and style, and remarks by dozens of poets.

The Discovery of Poetry, Frances Mayes, © 1987, Harcourt Brace Jovanovich. A comprehensive and thorough text on the reading and writing of poetry, with a clear introduction to poetry's art and craft.

For the Good of the Earth and Sun, Georgia Heard, © 1989, Heinemann. A very good text for teaching poetry to grades K-12. Many exercises and process notes. Offers a method for teaching poetry that respects the intelligence and originality of both teacher and student.

In the Palm of Your Hand, The Poet's Portable Workshop, Steve Kowit, © 1995, Tilbury House, Publishers. "A lively and illuminating guide for the practicing poet," as the cover states, with many lessons that can be easily adapted to teaching young poets.

poemcrazy: freeing your life with words, Susan Wooldridge, © 1996, Clarkson Potter. Excellent book by long-time CPITS poet-teacher, filled with many practice lessons, as well as observations on how poetry is found, and how it fits into everyday life. Important for its attitude as well as its content.

The Poet's Companion, Kim Addonizio and Dorianne Laux, © 1997, WW Norton & Co. A compendium of poetry lessons on craft and subjects (Sex, Death, Love, the Family, etc.) drawn from the authors' teaching experience. Includes interviews with contemporary poets, and model poems.

The Poetry Connection:An Anthology of Contemporary Poems with Ideas to Stimulate Children's Writing, Kinereth Gensler and Nina Nyhart, © 1978.An excellent double anthology of adult and children's poetry, cross-indexed with lessons and teaching approaches.

A Poetry Handbook, Mary Oliver, © 1994, Harcourt Brace & Co.A simple and exquisite explanation of craft by a foremost American poet.

Rising Voices, A Guide to Young Writers' Resources, Second Edition, Poets & Writers, Inc., NewYork. Up-to-date information about the best opportunities (including summer camps) for poets, fiction writers, and playwrights, K-12.A new section lists web sites and other on-line areas for young writers.

Starting with Little Things, A Guide to Writing Poetry in the Classroom, IngridWendt. Oregon Arts Foundation, 2111 Front St., NE, Ste. 210, Salem, OR 97303.A well-organized and practical handbook with 15 lessons, commentary, and poems by Oregon writers.

Writing Poetry, Barbara Drake, © 1983, Harcourt Brace Jovanovich.A solid handbook with 12 chapters full of teaching ideas, suggestions for writing, sample poems, a section on publishing, and a short bibliography.

BOOK SOURCES

California Poets in the Schools
870 Market St., Ste. 1148
San Francisco, CA 94102
(415) 399-1565

California Poets in the Schools features yearly anthologies of student and poet-teacher poetry from 1981 to the present.The last five publications are A Tree in the Sky, © 1995, Listen to the Wild, © 1996, Belonging to California, © 1997,Wilderness of Dreams, © 1998, and A Flame ofWords, © 1999. Each of these anthologies also contains lessons and essays on the art of teaching poetry writing. (Availability of some anthologies may be limited.)

OYATE
2702 Matthews St
Berkeley, CA 94702
(510) 848-6700

An organization of elders, artists, activists, educators, and writers who have come together to bring the real histories of the indigenous peoples of this continent to the attention of all Americans.Texts, resources, books, fiction, poetry, children's books and materials written and illustrated by Native people.Write for a catalogue, which includes storytelling work by Joseph Bruchac and poetry by Mary Tallmountain.There's also a book called Basic Skills Caucasian Americans Workbook.

Small Press Traffic
766 Valencia Street
San Francisco, CA 94110

Small Press Traffic is an excellent source of literary magazines and small press publications of poetry, most of which you can't find in larger bookstores.

Teaching Tolerance
Southern Poverty Law Center
400 Washington St
Montgomery, AL 36104

A quarterly magazine distributed free to all teachers (just write for it on letterhead) from the organization which has filed successful lawsuits against the KKK and Aryan Nation. This is full of valuable lesson ideas from other teachers; kids art and writing; and also a growing array of teaching tools (videos, posters, book lists) all on the subject of human tolerance. Inspired and inspiring.

Teachers and Writers Collaborative
5 Union Square West
New York, NY 10003-3306

Teachers and Writers has an excellent catalogue of books about teaching writing, and publishes many of them. They also put out a magazine with articles, lessons, and essays about teaching writing. Highly recommended as a resource.

VIDEO SOURCE

The American Poetry Archives
The Poetry Center
San Francisco State University
1600 Holloway Ave
San Francisco, CA 94132
(415) 338-1056

The American Poetry Archives rents and sells videotapes of all the poetry readings made by the Poetry Center since 1973, as well as of readings and interviews from the Lannan Literary Series, and of the outtakes of the 1960's NET series *USA: Poetry*. These consist of extensive interviews with major poets of that time, such as Charles Olson and Anne Sexton. An excellent way for students to see a wide range of varying backgrounds, styles, and voices. Catalogue available.

CPITS Board of Directors

CALIFORNIA
POETS IN THE
SCHOOLS

Susan Sibbet	*Poet-Teacher,* San Francisco *President*
Michael McLaughlin	*Poet-Teacher/CPITS Coordinator,* San Luis Obispo *Vice President*
Gina Mackintosh	*Development Consultant, Grants Plus,* San Francisco *Secretary and Interim Treasurer*
Danielle Alexich	*Poet/Teacher,* Chico
Lisa Busby	*Educator,* San Francisco
Albert DeSilver	*Poet-Teacher,* Woodacre
Lakeesha Gage	*Financial Assistant, Redefining Progress* *San Francisco State University student*
Georgette James	*Poet-Teacher,* San Diego
Mark Lambert	*Lawyer, Orrick, Herrington & Sutcliffe,* San Francisco
Nina Lindsay	*Librarian, Oakland Public Library,* *former CPITS student*
Diane Lutovich	*Advanced Communications Design,* Mill Valley
Scott Meltsner	*Poet/Teacher,* Elk
minerva	*Poet-Teacher,* San Diego
Chris Olander	*Poet Teacher/CPITS Area Coordinator,* Nevada City
Sojourner Kinkaid Rolle	*Poet-Teacher,* Santa Barbara

Staff

Mary Vradelis	*Executive Director*
Greg McCombs	*Development and Member Services*
Helen Vradelis	*Administrative Assistant*

THERE'S NO BETTER INVESTMENT

CALIFORNIA POETS IN THE SCHOOLS

CPITS needs your support. There are many ways you can help.

- Support your local poets!
- Encourage the creative writing, critical thinking, and self esteem of our children.
- Take time for your own poetry.
- Share and affirm the diversity of California by insuring that our schools bring culturally competent poets and multicultural materials into the classroom.
- Build partnerships between schools, the community, and poets and artists.

...And of course, become a *Friend of CPITS*. Please join at whatever level you can afford.

☐ $10,000 Angel		☐ $350 Leader	
☐ $5,000 Laureate		☐ $100 Sponsor	
☐ $1,000 Benefactor		☐ $50 Associate/Organization	
☐ $500 Patron		☐ $35 Contributor	

Name _____

Address _____

City/State/Zip _____

Phone (day) _____ - _____ (eve) _____ - _____

Signature _____ Date _____

VISA/MC # ☐☐☐☐ ☐☐☐☐ ☐☐☐☐ ☐☐☐☐ Expires on _____

Contributions of $35 or more will receive the current edition of CPITS' Statewide Anthology — the best of the amazing poetry children produce in CPITS' workshops annually all over the state. PLEASE MAKE CHECKS PAYABLE TO:

CPITS, 870 Market Street, Suite 1148, San Francisco, CA 94102.
Your contribution to CPITS is tax-deductible.

☐ Please send me more information on CPITS.

☐ I am a teacher. I teach at _____

in the county of _____

school address _____

phone _____ - _____

☐ I'd like to sponsor a poet residency for our school.

☐ I'd like to volunteer. Please contact me.

☐ My employer (or spouse's employer) will match my contribution to California Poets in the Schools.

☐ Enclosed is my signed matching gift form.

For more information, please call us at 415.399.1565 or e-mail: info@cpits.org

THANK YOU!